I Can See

Written by Adria Klein

Scholastic Inc.
New York Toronto London Auckland Sydney
Mexico City New Delhi Hong Kong

ISBN 0-439-13189-8

12 11 10 9 8 5/0
Printed in China 62

I can see a **red** ladybug.

I can see a **brown** bear.

I can see a yellow snake.

I can see a **gray** elephant.

I can see a **green** frog.

I can see a **black** whale.

What can you see?